)ND SON

jF
M   McDowell, Margaret Clemens
        Second son.

illustrated by

JEANYEE WONG

SECOND SON

by MARGARET CLEMENS McDOWELL

FRIENDSHIP PRESS   1956   NEW YORK

Words of "Planting Rice" in Chapter 3 used by permission of Silver Burdett Company, New York.

LIBRARY OF CONGRESS CATALOG CARD NUMBER: 55-11943

CONTENTS

MY NIPA HUT 1

A cloud of dust moved slowly along the narrow road that led from the rice paddy to the small Philippine village. Clump, clump, clump, in the middle of the cloud of dust walked a huge animal. It was a carabao, a water buffalo, with great curved horns. On its sides were hung bundles of rice stalks. On top of the broad back Pedro Garcia, known as Segundo, stretched out lazily. Segundo was only eight years old, but he knew just how to guide the big carabao by the rope that was fastened to a ring in the animal's nose.

"Ai, Generál," said Segundo, "we'll both be glad to get into the river." Segundo did not notice another dust cloud coming faster behind him. But soon he heard a sharp clump, clump of heavy feet. He sat up and looked back.

"It's that Ramón," he said. "He thinks to beat me home."

Ramón was waving a stick and whacking the sides of his animal. Though the carabao's hide was tough, he did not like this treatment. He shook his head and snorted.

"I'll beat you to the river!" shouted Ramón. "You can't expect to be first when you are only Segundo."

Segundo scowled. There were times when he did not like his nickname Segundo, which meant "the second one."

"If my big brother had lived, he would settle that Ramón," he thought.

But he only said shortly, "It's too hot to hurry."

"Yah!" yelled Ramón. He bounced up and down above his rice bundles as he jogged past.

Segundo kicked his bare feet against Generál's sides. "Please, Generál, can't you hurry?" he begged. Generál changed his pace from a slow walk to a slightly faster one.

"We'll never catch up," sighed Segundo.

Suddenly he began to laugh. With all the bouncing, the cord that had held the rice bundles on Ramón's carabao had come untied. Down into the road went the bundles of rice, and down on top of them went Ramón. The carabao, glad to be rid of his annoying load, jogged on toward home.

"Oy! Ho! Nuang!" cried Ramón. "Wait for me!" But the carabao did not stop.

Segundo was laughing as he rode past. "Your father will not like it that you dump the rice," he said.

"It wasn't my fault," sputtered Ramón.

"Well, if you get home in time for a swim, I'll see you in the river," said Segundo. He felt quite pleased. He did not worry about Ramón. It would soon be time for the midday *siesta* or rest. The other workers would be coming in from the rice paddies with their carabaos dragging wooden sleds on which the rice was piled. Segundo and Ramón had been sent on ahead with their smaller loads. Help would come to Ramón—in time.

"Go on home, Generál," said Segundo.

As they made their way around a bend in the road, Segundo saw two children coming toward him.

"Oho!" he said. "My sisters."

"Stop for us, Segundo," called Maria, who was two years older than her brother.

"We want a ride on Generál," said Dona, who was six.

"Hungh, Generál!" commanded Segundo, in a loud voice. "Stop!"

Stopping was one of the things Generál did best. He gladly came to a halt.

With Maria boosting and Segundo pulling, Dona was soon seated in front of her brother. It was harder for Maria to clamber up to a place behind, but with a strong pull from Segundo she made it.

"Ho, Generál!" cried Segundo, shaking the rope. "Go home." And so the three children rode into the clearing by the river where their house stood.

They could see Grandmother, tossing rice up and down in a shallow basket so that the wind would blow the chaff away. She sat in front of their house.

It was a pretty home, small and square, perched up in the air on posts. It had a steep thatched roof made of *nipa* palm, and sides of woven bamboo. It looked

something like a big basket turned upside down. A bamboo ladder led inside.

In the space underneath the house lived the chickens and two pigs. They liked this spot, for it was shady.

As Generál plodded through the opening in the bamboo fence around the yard, Segundo began to sing a song that all Filipino children know:

My *nipa* hut is very small,
But the foods that I grow—
see it houses them all!

Maria and Dona joined in, singing the names of the seeds one by one—turnips and eggplant, beans and peanuts.

Grandmother looked up as Generál brought the children closer to her.

"Hello!" she called, smiling at the singing children. "Segundo, after you unload the rice, you will just have time for your swim before dinner. Maria and Dona, I need your help. Angelina is washing the clothes."

"A swim will be good," answered Segundo. He and the girls slid down from Generál's back. Generál stood patiently as Segundo loosened the rope that held the rice bundles. Segundo peeled off his shirt and shorts. Holding his clothes under his arm, he jumped on Generál's back again.

"Come on, Generál!" he shouted.

When they reached the water's edge, Segundo tossed his clothes to the ground. Generál lumbered down to the river bank with him, passing a pretty girl who was on her knees beside the water. With a wooden paddle, she was beating a white shirt against a flat stone. This was Angelina, Segundo's oldest sister.

"Oh! You startled me," she laughed, as she gathered up the wet clothes. "It is well I finished before you and Generál came to muddy the water."

With snorts of satisfaction, Generál waded out to the middle of the river. Then slowly, slowly, he sank down. Soon all Segundo could see was the small black island upon which he sat, which was Generál's back; a tiny black spot up front, which was Generál's nose; and two sharp tips, which were the ends of Generál's horns.

Segundo stood up on his island. "Here I go!" he shouted, as he dived into the water.

For a while he swam about enjoying himself. At last he heard another splash. It was Ramón.

"Ai!" grinned Segundo. "You are late today."

"I would have got here first if that rope hadn't come untied," Ramón said.

"Well, you're here now," said Segundo, good-naturedly. "Come on, I'll race you to the bend in the river."

But Ramón knew that he was no match for Segundo at swimming. "It's too hot to hurry," he said, just as Segundo had said to him back on the road.

"Segundo!" Angelina called. "Come and get your dinner! If you want to eat outside, bring a banana leaf."

Suddenly Segundo realized that he was all one big emptiness inside. Leaving Generál in the water, he scrambled up the river bank, shook himself, and pulled on his clothes. From a tall banana plant he broke off a big, broad leaf. Then he ran toward the bamboo ladder.

Inside, Grandmother was stirring something in a big iron pot above some burning coals, which were held in a large earthen bowl set on a box of sand. Segundo's father and mother, who had been busy in the rice field all morning, were now home. They squatted on the floor before a low table. Angelina was setting plates filled with steaming rice and fish on the table.

"Mmmh! It smells good. I'm hungry," said Segundo.

"If everyone works well this afternoon, we can finish the rice. And tomorrow we can go to market," said Father.

"Oh! Fun!" cried Maria. "We'll help, won't we, Dona?"

They all loved to go to the market town. There was so much more to see and do than in the quiet little *barrio* that was their home village.

The children liked to eat their meals outside whenever possible, so for each one Grandmother spooned onto a broad piece of banana leaf a big helping of the rice and crisp fish. Angelina folded over the sides of the leaf to make a little package that could be carried easily. With it she handed each one a banana. The children hurried down the ladder and settled in the shade of the mango tree.

After dinner, everyone took a rest and slept. This is necessary in the Philippines, for it is very hot there in the middle of the day.

After the *siesta,* Father called them all to go back to work. By sundown the last bit of the rice was cut. When they reached home, Grandmother had supper ready for them.

"Children," said Mother, when they had finished eating, "we must go to bed early. See, it's already dark."

Sure enough, the fireflies were flashing their little lanterns against the dark of the mango tree.

"Tell us one story, please, Grandmother, before we go to bed," Segundo coaxed.

"Very well," said Grandmother. "I'll tell you about the clever monkey."

Dona put her head on Grandmother's lap, and Segundo and Maria sat on either side.

"Once upon a time," began Grandmother, "there was a wise old monkey who lived in a tree by the river. On the other side of the river the monkey could see a fine big banana plant full of ripe bananas.

" 'Mmmmh!' said the monkey. 'They look better than any bananas on this side. I must have them.' So he walked along until he saw a log lying across the river. The monkey ran quickly across on the log. He ran because he feared a crocodile might get him.

"The monkey ran to the banana plant. One after another he ate the big yellow bananas until he could hold no more.

" 'I am full,' said the monkey. 'I may as well go home.'

"He ran to the river's edge. The log was gone. In its place was a big crocodile with a wide-open mouth. Beside it were two small crocodiles.

" 'Now,' said the crocodiles, 'we shall have a good dinner.'

" 'But I am very small,' said the monkey. 'And you

are very large. And there are so many of you. I will not be enough to satisfy you.'

" 'Still we shall eat you,' said the big crocodile. 'Each of us will have a little piece. That will be better than nothing.'

"Then the monkey said, 'If you must eat me, you must. But first let me count you. I want to see how many crocodiles there are. Get in line across the river.'

"So the crocodiles got in line across the river. The monkey stepped on the first crocodile's back. He walked very slowly from its long nose to its tail.

" 'One,' he counted. 'This makes one crocodile.'

"Then the monkey stepped across to the second crocodile's back. Slowly he walked from its nose to its tail.

" 'Two,' he counted. 'This makes two crocodiles.'

"The monkey stepped across to the third crocodile's back. Slowly he walked from its nose to its tail.

" 'My friends,' he said, 'this makes THREE crocodiles.'

"As he said THREE, the monkey jumped quickly to

the bank of the river. He did not stop until he was safe in the branches of his own tree. The crocodiles could not reach the monkey. So they did not get their dinner. And that is the end of the story."

Segundo and Maria were laughing. "Thank you, Grandmother. That was a good story," said Maria.

"A funny one, too," agreed Segundo. "And that was a very clever monkey."

"Now bed for all of you," said Mother.

From a hanging shelf Mother took a *banig,* a sleeping mat, and spread it on the floor for Dona. Segundo and Maria unrolled their own *banigs,* and Mother spread netting over them all to keep off the mosquitoes.

"Monkeys are very clever," thought Segundo sleepily. "I wish I had one for a pet."

The last thing he heard was Father strumming his guitar and singing:

> My *nipa* hut is very small,
> But the foods that I grow—
> see it houses them all!

2 MARKET DAY

"Hurry, Generál! We are almost there!" Once again Segundo kicked his feet against Generál's broad sides. But Generál paid little attention. He had been pulling the heavy cart since sunrise, and now that they had at last reached the town he did not intend to get excited about it.

Segundo was in his usual place astride Generál's back. Father and Mother and Angelina sat on the board seat in the front of the cart. On her lap Mother held a basket of eggs. Maria and Dona stood up in back, among the things Father was taking to market. There were a large basket of fruit from the mango tree and a smaller one of squash from Mother's garden. There was a pile of large straw hats that Grandmother had woven. Three hens clucked and scolded in a bamboo cage.

"This way, Generál!" cried Segundo, pulling on the rope. Generál turned into a side street near the market place and stopped. Segundo slid from his back, and everyone piled out of the cart. Father fastened Generál's rope to a post. Then he looked at the things in the cart.

"I will have to come back for the hens," he said. "Segundo, you must stay and watch them." He gave some of the hats to Maria and some to Dona. The basket of squash he lifted to Angelina's head. He picked up the heavy basket of mangoes, and Mother carried the eggs. Segundo watched them all disappear around the corner.

In a few minutes Father was back. "We found a fine place," he said. "Now help me with the hens."

Segundo climbed into the cart and boosted the cage of scolding hens over the side to his father. Then he followed him to the market place.

The market place was a large open square, already crowded with people. In the center were rows of open booths or shops, filled with all kinds of wonderful articles for sale. Around the edges were open places where people from the *barrios* could spread out their produce.

The Garcias had indeed found a good place, and Mother already had a customer. A woman was looking at the eggs. "Are they fresh?" she asked.

"We sell only fresh eggs," Mother answered.

"You look like honest people," said the woman. "I'll take some eggs." She placed a few eggs in her basket and counted some money into Mother's hand.

In the meantime Father reached into his pocket and brought out three coins. "A *sinco* for each of you," he said smiling, as he handed them to the three children. "You can buy some sweets. Go on now, and have a good time."

The children waited for no second invitation to be off to see the sights. Segundo led the way past the country people who were squatting on their heels behind baskets of all kinds of fruits—bananas and pineapples and mangoes—and of vegetables—beans and squash and turnips. There were bamboo crates of ducks and hens, and young pigs with their legs tied together.

But Segundo and Maria and Dona wanted to visit the little booths, for many of the things here came from the big city of Manila. They pushed on through the crowd, holding tightly to their *sincos.*

So much there was to see! They passed booths where people were selling straw hats and bamboo baskets, mosquito nets and straw *banigs,* fresh fish and cooked locusts. Segundo and Maria and Dona took turns picking out things they would like to buy if they had plenty of money.

"Ai! How pretty!" exclaimed Maria. "See these beautiful earrings! I choose them."

"Girls choose such silly, useless things," said Segundo in disgust. "Now I would take that beautiful *bolo.*" He pointed to a large knife with a handle of carabao horn.

"You would like this fine *bolo?*" asked the shopkeeper.

"I would like it," said Segundo honestly. "But I don't have enough money."

"Then be on your way," said the man crossly.

Dona looked frightened, but Maria took her hand.

"It's all right, Dona," she said. "Come on, I wouldn't buy his old earrings if I had a hundred *sincos*."

The next booth was the best yet, for here were the kind of sweets that children love. Segundo felt his mouth water as he looked. There were bamboo baskets holding pieces of sugar cane about two feet long. People bought them, peeled off the shiny bark, and chewed the soft fiber to get the sweet juice inside. There were sticks of sweetened rice and a kind of candy made of coconut and brown sugar. There were small coconut cakes and boxes of sweet brown sugar.

"Mmmmh!" said Segundo. Surely this was the place to spend his *sinco*.

"Mmmmh!" said Maria and Dona, their eyes big and round.

"Take your time," said the woman in charge.

Finally Maria and Dona decided on coconut candy. The young woman wrapped two pieces for each in a bit of banana leaf and fastened the leaf with a splinter of bamboo.

"And now, young man, what will you have?" she asked Segundo. "Some sugar cane?"

"Some sugar cane and two pieces of candy for my *sinco*," said Segundo.

"For one *sinco* you may have a sugar cane stick and one piece of candy," she said.

Segundo agreed, pleased at the bargain. He put the candy into his pocket and went off chewing his sugar cane.

Maria and Dona paused at a booth where bright colored dress material was on sale. "Let's choose what we would like for new dresses," suggested Maria.

This did not interest Segundo. "I'll go on," he said. "You can catch up later."

And that is how he happened to find the best thing of all.

It was in a booth where pineapples and bananas were hanging from the roof. In a bamboo cage at one side were several little green parrots that interested him. But he did not like the looks of the shopkeeper, a large dark man, who rubbed his hands together as he called, "A *paro*, a *paro!* Come and buy a nice *paro* for a pet!"

Suddenly Segundo saw the man reach out with his foot and kick something.

"Get out of my way, you nuisance!" he growled.

As Segundo looked, he saw a little monkey scamper over to the front corner of the booth, as far from the man as possible. He sat hunched up, covering his wrinkled face with his little black paws,

looking very miserable. Segundo saw that he was tied to a post by a rope fastened to a leather strap around his small body.

Quickly Segundo squatted down beside the little creature. "Little monkey, look at me," he said softly. "Don't be afraid."

As if he understood, the monkey took his paws

27

away from his face and stared at Segundo with his beady black eyes.

Segundo patted one of the little black paws. "Nice monkey," he said. Suddenly he remembered the candy in his pocket. He fed it to the monkey, bit by bit, talking to him as he did so. The shopkeeper was too busy to notice.

Finally Segundo thought of his sisters. They must see this wonderful thing. "Don't go away. I'll be right back," he said to the monkey.

Maria and Dona had just decided that they liked the material with pink roses better than that with blue ones when Segundo came running to them.

"Come quick!" he said. "Come see the monkey I found!"

"A monkey!" exclaimed Maria. "Where is it?"

Segundo pulled his sisters through the crowd. "Here," he said. "This is the place." Just as they arrived, they saw the monkey dart up the pole to which he was tied. With one skinny paw he reached out and pulled a banana from the nearest bunch. Quickly he peeled it and stuffed the fruit into his mouth.

Dona clapped her hands, and Maria said, "Oh, isn't he cute!"

The monkey threw the banana peel. It hit the shopkeeper squarely on the top of his head. The children laughed in delight. But the shopkeeper did not laugh. A scowl spread over his face, and he grabbed a stick.

"You little thief!" he cried. "I'll teach you to steal my bananas!" He struck the monkey, who scrambled down the pole and ran as far as his rope would let him.

By that time Segundo had reached his side. The monkey saw the boy who had given him candy. With one leap he landed in Segundo's arms. He fastened his hairy little arms around Segundo's neck and clung tightly.

"Get out of the way, you boy!" yelled the shopkeeper.

But Segundo turned his back and held the monkey close. "You can't hit him again!" he cried. "He's so little."

"I can't, can't I?" roared the man. "Get out of the way, or you'll get it, too!"

Segundo did not move, and the man brought the stick down across his back. Dona began to cry, but Segundo held tightly to the monkey.

"What's going on here?" cried a new voice. A well dressed man came hurrying up. "What are you doing with my monkey?" he asked Segundo.

Before Segundo could explain, the shopkeeper began to speak. He had dropped his stick, and he smiled at the man as he rubbed his hands together. "Sir, I caught this boy trying to steal your monkey," he said.

"What do you mean?" the man asked Segundo sternly. "I should have you arrested."

"Why—I—I—wasn't stealing him," stammered Segundo.

"The boy is right," said several people in the crowd that had gathered. One man explained. "The man struck the monkey because he took a banana. This boy tried to save him. He got a stick across his back for it."

The monkey's owner turned to the shopkeeper. "Is this the truth?" he demanded.

The shopkeeper looked at the angry crowd. He

saw he would have to tell the truth. "I only hit him a little tap," he said uneasily. "He stole a banana."

"Take that for your banana," exclaimed the man scornfully. He tossed a coin at the shopkeeper. "I told you I would pay you well if you found a kind owner for my pet. And you do it by beating him!"

"But, Sir—but, Sir—" began the shopkeeper.

The stranger paid no attention. "What is your name, Boy?" he asked Segundo.

"Pedro Garcia, Sir, but I am called Segundo," answered Segundo, still holding the monkey close.

"Well, Segundo," said the man smiling, "you are a brave boy, and I can see that you like animals. How would you like to have Ongoy for a pet?"

"Oh, Sir, I would like it more than anything in the world," said Segundo earnestly. "But I cannot buy him, for I have no money."

"I don't want money for him," said the man. "I want a good, kind master, for I am leaving the island this week."

Segundo's eyes were shining. "Sir," he promised, "I'll be kind to Ongoy."

"I believe you will, Boy," said the man. He untied the rope and handed it to Segundo.

"There you are, Segundo," he said. "Treat Ongoy well. And if the time comes when you cannot keep him, take him out to the forest and set him free."

The man patted the monkey gently. "Good-by, little friend. Good-by, Ongoy," he said. Then he hurried away.

The people began to move on. Segundo stood still, his arms about the little monkey. He could not believe his good fortune. Maria and Dona patted the monkey timidly.

"Is he really yours?" asked Dona, her eyes big with wonder.

"I—I—I think so," stuttered Segundo.

"Of course he is, silly," said Maria. "Didn't everyone hear the man say so?"

"Come! We must show Ongoy to Father and Mother."

The three children hurried off, Ongoy riding on Segundo's shoulder.

STRANGERS IN THE BARRIO 3

Segundo sat at his desk in the small one-roomed school. The third grade children were writing compositions.

"A monkey is a very nice pet," Segundo wrote.

The fifth grade was ready to report. Segundo noticed Maria's hand waving wildly in the air.

"Yes, Maria," said Miss Reyes, the teacher. "You may tell us."

Maria stood up. "The Philippines is a republic," she said. "We elect our own president. Our country is made up of more than seven thousand islands. Many are very small, and no one lives on them. The largest one is—"

"Very good," interrupted Miss Reyes. "Juan may name the seven largest islands."

Segundo sighed. Maria knew a great deal—

for a girl! He wrote, "I have a monkey named Ongoy." What should he say next? There was so much to tell about Ongoy.

Segundo remembered how at first he had tied Ongoy's rope to one of the house posts. But Ongoy had jumped on the back of one of the pigs, scaring him half to death. Then he had stolen and eaten an egg.

Everyone had laughed at these antics, but Mother said it would not do to lose the eggs. So Father tied Ongoy to the mango tree. Each day Segundo took him water and rice in coconut shells, and always a banana for a treat.

Still, Ongoy looked a little like a prisoner, being always tied up. Segundo wondered how he could write this.

"Segundo! Segundo! Wake up!" It was the voice of Miss Reyes. "Come, it is time for singing."

Segundo came to with a start. The other children were standing beside their desks. Everyone was laughing at him.

Segundo's face was red as he got to his feet.

"Ai, Segundo," whispered Ramón behind him,

in a teasing voice, "you're not even second today!"

"We'll sing the rice song," said Miss Reyes. "You may act it out as we sing."

The children liked this—bending and stepping, bending and stepping, as they sang:

> Planting rice is never fun,
> Bent from morn 'til set of sun;
> Cannot stand and cannot sit,
> Cannot rest for a little bit.

It was because of the singing that no one heard the jeep come down the road and stop at the schoolhouse. But everyone heard the knock at the door.

"Take your seats, children," said Miss Reyes, as she went to answer it.

Soon she was back, followed by two men. Segundo was sure the older one was an American. The younger one was a tall Filipino youth. For some reason, Segundo liked this boy at once.

"Children," said Miss Reyes, "this is Mr. Marks. He has something to tell us."

The older man stood smiling at the children.

"Hello, boys and girls," he said. "Your teacher is kind to let us come in. We come from the Christian mission station near the big city. I am a missionary teacher there, and my young friend is a student. He is Carlos Cruz."

Carlos waved a friendly hand.

"We invite everyone in the *barrio* to a meeting this evening in the schoolyard," went on Mr. Marks. "Tell your fathers and mothers there will be singing and Bible stories and lantern pictures. And I want to talk to the men about farming."

Mr. Marks paused. "Can you remember all that to tell your families?" he asked.

The children nodded. Their eyes were bright. Seldom did such a thing as a meeting take place in their small *barrio*.

Miss Reyes smiled at their excitement. "It is almost time for school to close, so you may be excused a little early today," she said.

The children got to the door quietly, but they fairly tumbled down the steps. The boys gathered around the jeep.

"I wonder how you start it?" said Juan.

"This is the horn," said Mario, pointing to a large button.

"Let's see if it is," said Ramón, reaching for the button.

Suddenly Segundo felt that someone should watch over the property of these visitors. "No," he said, grabbing Ramón's arm. "We should leave it alone, Ramón."

Carlos came out of the schoolhouse in time to hear. He understood how boys want to know about anything that runs. "I'll show you the horn," he said. "Here, Ramón, you may blow it. This button turns on the light. This starts the motor."

The boys watched with interest. Then Carlos turned to Segundo. "What's your name?" he asked.

"Segundo, Sir," answered the boy.

The young man smiled. "Call me Carlos," he said. Then to the group, "Segundo was right. No one should fool with a car until he is old enough to drive it. And now, how about taking that invitation home to your parents? Mr. Marks and I must get ready for

38

tonight. If you'll come early, we can play some games before the meeting."

The children began to move away, but Segundo waited.

"C-c-ould I help you g-g-get ready?" he asked. Segundo stuttered a bit, as he sometimes did when he was excited.

"Sure," said Carlos with a smile. "I need a helper. We'll make camp first. Hop in, and I'll back over."

Segundo climbed in and watched as the older boy backed the car carefully to the far side of the school-yard.

"What a car!" he thought. "Backwards as well as forwards it can go!"

By the time Mr. Marks came out, Carlos and Segundo had unloaded a small tent, two folding cots, and two mosquito nets. Soon everything was in place.

"I think, Sir," said Carlos to Mr. Marks, "the pictures will show up well on the schoolhouse wall. Shall I set up the projector?"

"What is a pro-pro—a—what you said?" asked Segundo.

"It is a machine that will show pictures on the wall," explained Carlos. "Our electric power is here in the jeep."

Carlos unpacked a folding table and a small black machine.

"Now, Segundo," he said, "watch the schoolhouse wall."

Segundo looked at the blank wall, and suddenly it was blank no longer. On it were the faint outlines of a picture in soft colors. Segundo could make out a woman leaning over a baby.

"It's the Baby Jesus and Mary," said Carlos.

Segundo gazed in wonder. "Is it magic?" he whispered.

"No, it is not magic," laughed Carlos. "But wait and see how it looks tonight." He snapped a switch, and the wall was blank again. Then he asked, "Do you know where I can get some water?"

"Yes," said Segundo. "There is a good spring near here."

Segundo led the way down the road and off onto a well worn path. Ahead, the path forked into two trails. Then Segundo saw a little lizard and stooped to watch it.

"Come on, Segundo," called Carlos, turning to the left. "The spring is this way."

"Yes," agreed Segundo in surprise. "The other path leads to Ramón's house."

A few feet beyond they came to the spring. The water flowed out from the steep bank above. A long piece of split bamboo guided it down to where it could be reached.

"It's a wonderful spring," said Carlos, as he filled his bamboo pail. "It looks familiar somehow. I must have seen one like it somewhere."

Segundo asked a question that was puzzling him. "How did you know the left path led to the spring?"

Carlos laughed. "I don't know," he said. "Just a good guess, I suppose."

Back on the road Segundo left his new friend and hurried home. He found everyone excited about the meeting. Even Grandmother was going. Never before had pictures been shown in this *barrio*. Segundo felt very important as he told how he had been helping, and how he had touched the machine that made pictures.

No one lingered over the meal. The children hurried back for games. Carlos knew many good ones, and they had so much fun they did not notice the older people coming.

At last Carlos blew a whistle. "Time for the meeting to begin," he said. "We'll have to stop now."

The children hurried to find places with their parents, who were squatting on their heels or sitting on the ground.

Mr. Marks began to speak. He told about the mission school where boys and girls received Christian training, the hospital where sick people were helped, and the farm where students learned the best ways of raising food. His special work, he explained, was teaching farming.

Everyone listened, and everyone was surprised. There was no church in their small *barrio,* yet they all knew about the big church in the market town, where people went to get married and to take their gifts and to pray sometimes. But they had never heard of anyone from there coming out to help the sick or to teach them to be better farmers.

Mr. Marks guessed what they were thinking. "Jesus came to help all people," he said. "If they were sick, he helped them to be well. When they were hungry, he gave them food. When they did wrong, he showed them a better way.

"We who are Jesus' followers want to help as he did," he went on. "We want to share with you the Bible teachings and stories. Our doctors and nurses want to help you to be strong and well. And if we can find ways to raise more and better food, there will be fewer hungry people on these islands."

The people nodded, pleased.

"Tomorrow," said Mr. Marks at last, "I will visit you as you work. Now let me tell you why Carlos is here.

"During the vacation season," he explained, "the mission sends its students to different *barrios* to hold vacation Bible schools for the children for two weeks. There are Bible stories and songs and games and other interesting things. Carlos will call at your homes tomorrow to find out if you would like him to have such a school here."

Of course they would want it, thought Segundo happily. Two whole weeks with Carlos!

"And now," Mr. Marks was saying, "it is dark enough for our pictures."

Segundo looked around in surprise. Sure enough, the fireflies were showing against the dark trees.

Carlos stepped over to the projector and turned something. A large square of light appeared on the schoolhouse wall. Suddenly there was a beautiful picture in the square of light. It showed a baby asleep on a bed of straw. A lovely woman was bent over him. It was the picture Segundo had seen earlier, but now it was clear and bright.

"This is Jesus, God's best gift to us," began Mr. Marks. There were other pictures, and Mr. Marks explained them all as the people looked and listened.

Finally the meeting was over. "Good night, everyone," called Mr. Marks. "Carlos and I hope to see you tomorrow."

The Garcias were the last family to go. Before they

left, Father and Mother invited Mr. Marks and Carlos to their home for dinner the next day.

Segundo edged close to Carlos. "D-d-do you need someone to help you tomorrow?" he asked.

Carlos rumpled the smaller boy's dark hair. "Indeed I do," he said. "I need someone to show me where all the homes are. I'll look for you early in the morning."

4 A DAY WITH CARLOS

Early the next morning, Segundo appeared at the camp near the schoolhouse.

"Hi!" called Mr. Marks. Then he looked carefully at the tall boy and the smaller one. "Do you know," he said in surprise, "you fellows look enough alike to be brothers!"

"Poor Segundo!" laughed Carlos. "Well, we're off to enroll the children for the vacation Bible school. Come on, Segundo. You're the guide."

As they walked along, Carlos asked, "How did you come to be called Segundo? You aren't the second child in the family, for I met your two older sisters last night."

"It's a nickname," said Segundo. "My real name is Pedro."

"Why are you called 'the second one'?" Carlos asked again.

"I am the second son," said Segundo. "I had a brother, but he was lost in the river when he was very small. It was before I was born."

"Oh!" exclaimed Carlos. "I'm sorry, Segundo."

"I would like to have a big brother," said Segundo. "Like you. My brother's name was Carlos, too."

"Most every family has a Carlos," said the older boy. "Tell you what, Segundo. Let's adopt each other." He smiled his warm, friendly smile at Segundo.

"I would like that," said Segundo, smiling back at Carlos.

All day the two went from home to home. Carlos told about the school. He wrote down the names of children who would come.

Only two mothers hesitated to say yes. Mrs. Santos declared, "My church would not want my children to go."

Carlos looked at the family of children—Pablo and Pacito and Josefina and Manuel. "We're going to have such a good time, Mrs. Santos," he said. "Why don't you come with your children for a few days. If you see any harm in what we teach, you can take them home."

This seemed fair to Mrs. Santos. "Perhaps I can do that," she agreed.

But Mrs. Rivera said firmly, "No. My Filberto may not go. It is not our religion."

"I am sorry, Mrs. Rivera," said Carlos. "We all worship the same God. But let us be friends anyway. Here are some Bible pictures for Filberto."

"Poor Filberto," said Segundo, as they started away.

"Perhaps by the time our school is over, Mrs. Rivera will trust us," said Carlos. "Then Filberto may be able to come next year."

By midafternoon they had visited every home.

"Now I can show you Ongoy," said Segundo. "And we can have a swim."

When they reached the Garcia home, Carlos took time first to speak politely to Mother, Grandmother, and Angelina, who were busy preparing dinner.

"It was good of you to invite Mr. Marks and me," said Carlos.

48

"We are happy to have you," smiled Mother. "Once I had a son named Carlos."

"Your second son told me," said Carlos. "It is sad."

"Ai, yes!" said Grandmother. "It is hard to believe, but our Carlos would have been eighteen years old now. I always think of him as a small one."

Carlos began talking about the vacation school, but soon he said, "Segundo and I are going for a swim."

"Ongoy first," said Segundo. He held the rope as they petted the little monkey. Ongoy scolded when they left him.

"Poor little thing!" said Carlos.

"I take good care of him," said Segundo. "I love him."

"I know you do," said Carlos. "But Ongoy is a little wild thing, used to being free. That's why I am sorry for him."

This was a new idea to Segundo, and he did not like it.

"Come and see our carabao," he said, leading the way to General's stall. Carlos patted the big animal.

"Hi there, Capitán!" he said.

"No, no!" said Segundo. "Not Capitán. This is Generál."

Carlos laughed and made a deep bow in Generál's direction. "Excuse my mistake, Generál," he said.

Carlos and Segundo found Ramón and Juan already in the water. They all had fun together.

"Carlos," asked Segundo, when the others had left, "why did you call our carabao Capitán?"

"Oh, I don't know," laughed Carlos, splashing water on Segundo. "It just seemed a good name for that carabao."

"Well, it's funny," said Segundo, splashing back, "because that was the name of the carabao we used to have. Capitán got old and died, and Father got Generál."

At that moment Juan called, "Segundo! Come quickly!"

"Now what?" said Segundo. "I'll bet it's that Ramón!"

He and Carlos swam to the shore and quickly pulled on their clothes. As they climbed up over the bank, they saw Juan and Ramón standing by the mango tree, looking up into the branches. Ongoy's rope was lying on the ground.

"Where's Ongoy?" demanded Segundo.

"He got away," said Juan miserably.

"How did he get away?" Segundo asked angrily.

Juan looked at Ramón. "Tell him the truth," he said.

"I was only going to pet him," said Ramón. "I untied the rope from his strap, but I didn't mean to let him get away."

"He climbed up into the tree," added Juan.

Suddenly they heard Ongoy's chatter far up in the branches. "Maybe I can get him," said Segundo, starting to climb.

"Let me go, little brother," said Carlos.

"No, please," said Segundo. "Ongoy knows me. I think he will come for me."

Higher and higher climbed Segundo, stepping from bough to bough, and shinnying up over places where there were no branches. He called softly as he climbed. But always overhead came that teasing chatter-chatter. Finally Segundo reached the branch on which Ongoy was sitting. He straddled it as he coaxed, "Come, Ongoy. Come here."

But Ongoy sat still, watching with his beady little eyes. Carefully Segundo worked his way along the branch. He stretched out a hand but couldn't quite reach. He moved a little farther out, and the branch dipped.

"Careful, Segundo!" cried Carlos sharply.

It was too late. There was a sharp crack. With an excited cry, Ongoy leaped for another branch. But Segundo was not a monkey. He came crashing down through the branches.

Carlos ran for the spot where he thought Segundo would fall and held out his arms. Segundo plunged into them, knocking Carlos to the ground, too.

Carlos recovered his breath first. He bent over the smaller boy, who lay still, his left arm folded under him.

"Are you hurt, little brother?" he asked anxiously.

Segundo was getting his breath again. "My—my —my arm hurts," he said.

Carlos looked at Segundo's left arm. The wrist was swelling.

"Can you move it?" he asked.

Segundo moved his hand. "I can, but it hurts," he said.

At that moment Segundo's father and Mr. Marks came into the yard. Quickly Carlos explained. "I shouldn't have let him climb the tree," he said.

"You couldn't have stopped him," said Father, patting Segundo's head. "This one climbs like a monkey himself."

"I think it is only a sprain," said Mr. Marks. "But I am not a doctor, and I cannot be sure."

Father carried Segundo into the house. Mother found a piece of cloth, and Mr. Marks made a sling. Now the pain was not so bad, but Segundo's face was white.

"Does it hurt so much?" asked Carlos.

"It's not that," said Segundo. "I've lost Ongoy."

At last they all gathered to enjoy the good dinner.

"You will say grace, please, Mr. Marks?" Father said. Mr. Marks thanked God for food and for friends and for the fact that Segundo had not been more badly hurt.

"Carlos saved me," said Segundo at the end of the prayer. "He caught me."

It was a fine dinner. One of the hens had been cooked with rice, and there was squash, and fruit for dessert. Segundo was so busy eating, with Dona trying to help, that he did not notice when Maria slipped out.

After a while she came in again, holding Ongoy.

"Oh! How did you do it?" exclaimed Segundo.

"I coaxed him with a banana," said Maria. "I guess he was ready to come." Segundo smiled his thanks. That Maria was a smart one, he thought.

After the meal was eaten, Mr. Marks looked at Segundo's swollen wrist. It was beginning to show black and blue.

"I wish our doctor could see it," he said. Then he straightened up. "Well, why not?" he asked. "Segundo can go to the mission with us tomorrow. In two weeks I will come back here with Carlos. We can bring Segundo home then."

He turned to Father and Mother. "Do let him come," he said. "Mrs. Marks will look after him, and our children, Dean and Nancy, will be pleased to have a visitor."

Mother looked worried. "Is his wrist bad?" she asked.

"I think it's only a sprain," answered Mr. Marks. "But I would like our good doctor to see it to make sure. Mrs. Marks and I will care for Segundo."

"I'll help," said Carlos. "I'll be his big brother."

Segundo was listening in astonishment. He could not believe his ears. Were they saying he might go with Carlos and Mr. Marks—in the jeep—to visit the mission—to stay two whole weeks? It couldn't be true!

But it was. Father and Mother said yes. Grandmother declared it would be a fine thing for him. And Angelina hurried to the chest to find his best khaki shorts and white T shirt, as if he were to start that minute.

"Maria and I will take care of Ongoy," offered Dona.

"And we'll keep that Ramón away!" snapped Maria.

"That Ramón!" echoed Segundo. "I'll get even with him."

"Want to know a good way to get even?" Carlos asked.

"Sure," said Segundo, wondering what fine plan Carlos had.

"Do something nice for him," said Carlos.

"What!" exclaimed Segundo.

"Ramón likes to tease," said Carlos. "The best way to turn him into a friend is to do something for him."

Segundo looked puzzled. This was hard to understand.

"We'll talk about it another time," said Carlos. "You've had about enough for one day."

"We'll stop for Segundo early in the morning," said Mr. Marks. "I hope the pain won't keep him awake."

Hmmp, thought Segundo, as he lay on his *banig*. What was a little pain? He really ought—ought—to thank—Ramón. But—he was—very sleepy—

5 A DIFFERENT WORLD

"Come, little son, wake up!"

Segundo opened his eyes. His mother was shaking him gently.

"Wake up!" she called. "How is your arm this morning?"

Segundo moved his wrist. It was stiff and sore, but it did not hurt very much. "It feels better," he said.

"It looks better," agreed Mother. "Come now. Dress quickly. You must be ready when Mr. Marks comes."

Everyone was up, and by the time breakfast was over, the jeep pulled into the yard. "Good morning, everyone!" called Mr. Marks. "How is our boy today?"

"Better," said Mother, smiling.

"Perhaps," said Father, "you should not bother to take Segundo with you."

Segundo's heart sank. Was he to miss the trip after all?

But Mr. Marks smiled. "Please let him come, Mr. Garcia," he said. "I would like the doctor to examine his wrist. And we really want Segundo to visit us."

So they were off. Segundo, sitting behind Mr. Marks and Carlos, waved good-by to his family with his good arm.

Segundo had never had a ride in a jeep before. After Generál's slow pace, the trees seemed to fly past at a dizzy speed. In no time they were through the market town, and speeding along roads Segundo had never seen. The sun climbed high, and they stopped for lunch. Then they were off again.

The road became wider and smoother. There were more homes, some larger and finer even than the landlord's house at home. On the road were not only carabao carts but horse drawn carriages and cars as well. Segundo kept turning his head from side to side so as to miss nothing.

It was late when the jeep finally turned into a drive-way lined with trees.

"Now we are on the mission property," said Mr.
Marks.

They drove past a large building with many windows. Two young women in white dresses were
walking toward it.

"This is our hospital," explained Carlos. "And
there are two of our nurses."

Next they passed several homes. "We live here,"
said Mr. Marks. "Wait until Dean and Nancy dis-
cover they have a visitor."

"On beyond"—Carlos waved toward more build-
ings—"are the school and the mission farm. You
have much to see."

Segundo felt that he was in a different world.

The jeep slowed to a stop before the last house,
and the door burst open. Two children came racing
out with shouts of, "Hi, Daddy! Hello, Carlos!" A
small dog tore after them. Last of all, a tall woman
came hurrying down the walk.

Mr. Marks and Carlos jumped out. As Segundo

waited, suddenly very shy, he saw that Dean was a little taller than himself. Nancy was about Dona's size.

"Come, little brother," Carlos said.

"Indeed, yes," said Mr. Marks. "Here, youngsters. We have a surprise for you." Quickly Mr. Marks introduced Segundo and explained why he had come.

Mrs. Marks put an arm around him. "We're so glad to have you," she said. "Come in now. I know you are tired and hot and hungry." Mrs. Marks understood that many things in their home would be strange to a small boy who had never even seen a bathroom before. "Carlos," she went on, "since Segundo must be careful of his arm, why don't you help him take a shower? I'll fix something to eat."

The shower, with water coming down all over him like a sudden rainfall, was wonderful. Carlos rubbed Segundo dry with a big towel and helped him dress. They went to the dining room, where food was ready. Strange food, it seemed to Segundo. But it was stranger yet to sit on a big chair and eat from a high table. Mrs. Marks poured milk for him.

"When we finish, I would like to take Segundo over to Dr. Brown," said Mr. Marks, "and ask him to look at that wrist."

Dean and Nancy chattered happily. "I'm glad you've come, Segundo," said Dean. "We'll have fun together."

After the meal, Carlos left. Segundo felt a sinking in his stomach as his friend walked out, but Mr. Marks said quickly, "Come on, youngsters. Let's go find Dr. Brown."

Mr. Marks led the way to Dr. Brown's house, with Nancy holding his hand. Segundo walked beside Dean, while the little dog Chip pranced at their feet. Segundo stopped to pat Chip.

"I have a pet monkey," he said to Dean.

"Oh, a monkey must be fun!" answered Dean.

Before Segundo had finished telling about Ongoy, they found Dr. Brown. He had a kind face and smiling blue eyes, and Segundo liked him at once. The doctor took Segundo's arm from the sling and examined the wrist.

"It doesn't hurt very much now," said Segundo.

"Well," said the doctor, "I believe there is no injury here that a few days' time won't cure. Just to be sure, though, we'll take an X ray at the hospital tomorrow. Do you know what an X ray is?"

Segundo shook his head.

"It's a picture that will let us look at the bone in your wrist." Dr. Brown smiled at Segundo.

Segundo's feet were dragging by the time they reached the house again. Mrs. Marks looked at him. "It has been a long day for our travelers," she said. "Let's have family prayers, and then the children must get to bed."

Here was something else new to Segundo. He listened with interest as Mr. Marks read a few verses from the Bible and then spoke of the friendliness they had met on their trip. He told how kind Miss Reyes had been, and how the landlord had offered the use of a big shed on his property for the vacation school. All they needed now was to make bamboo benches for the children. Then he thanked God for the good trip they had had and for all the friendliness in the world.

"Now off to bed," said Mrs. Marks with a smile.

"Come on, Segundo," said Dean. "It's lucky I have a double-deck bed. Do you want the upper bunk or the lower?"

Segundo gazed in alarm at the top bunk. He was used to sleeping on the floor. Could anyone sleep safely on that high shelf? "I'll t-t-take the lower shelf, please," he said.

"Sure," said Dean. "I like the upper."

Dean fell asleep at once, but though Segundo was tired, it took him longer. He tossed and turned. Finally he stepped quietly out of bed and lay down on the floor beside the bunk. In no time he was asleep.

In the morning Dean rushed out of the bedroom alone.

"Where's Segundo?" he cried. "He's already up."

Mr. and Mrs. Marks looked surprised.

"Are you sure?" asked Mrs. Marks. "He isn't out here."

They all hurried into Dean's room. Yes, the bed was empty! Where was Segundo?

"Woof! Woof!" barked Chip at the end of the bed.

He gently nipped at something sticking out beneath.

"Aow! Let go of my toe!" came a muffled cry, and two black eyes peered out from under the bed.

"Where am I?" asked Segundo.

Mr. Marks pulled him up as they all laughed.

"What are you doing under the bed?" he asked.

Segundo was embarrassed. "The b-b-bed was s-so high and s-so soft," he explained. "I thought I would sleep on the floor. I guess I rolled under it while I was asleep."

Mrs. Marks understood. "Why, of course, Segundo. I should have thought," she said. "Tonight you will have a *banig* to sleep on. Come now and have some breakfast."

What a breakfast it was! Pineapple juice, cereal, an egg, toast, and milk. Segundo enjoyed it all.

After breakfast Mr. Marks hurried off to the mission farm, and Dean and Nancy went to school. "This afternoon you can go with us," said Dean.

Segundo played with Chip until Mrs. Marks could take him to the hospital. There Dr. Brown and Miss Panay, the nurse, told him just what to do while they took a picture of his arm bone. Segundo was interested in all that happened.

After the X ray had been taken, Mrs. Marks wanted to visit some of the patients in the hospital. Dr. Brown said Segundo might go with her. Mrs. Marks had a friendly word for each one. At last they came back to see Dr. Brown again.

"Come and look at your X ray picture, Son," said Dr. Brown. "Do you see that good sound bone? No trouble there! In a few days you won't know you had a sprain."

In the afternoon Segundo went to school with Dean. After school some of the boys stayed to play ball together.

Because his wrist was still weak, Segundo could only watch this first day. He could hardly wait until he would be able to play, too. He was sitting on the ground at one side when he saw Carlos coming.

"Hi!" said Carlos. "Want to come and see the farm?"

"Oh, yes! I'd like to!" said Segundo, jumping to his feet.

It was Dean's turn to bat. "I'll stay," he said. "See you later, Segundo."

The farm was indeed a wonderful place, with cows, pigs, chickens, and even a big carabao. Each kind of animal had its own house or barn.

"I am learning all I can," explained Carlos. "Some day I hope to be able to help our people to be better farmers."

"I would like to be a doctor," said Segundo, thinking of Dr. Brown and his visit to the hospital.

"Fine!" said Carlos. "We need more doctors."

Before they had seen everything, it was time to eat. "I must take you home, little brother," said Carlos. "There will be another day."

Yes, there was another day, and another, and another. As each one went flying past, Segundo found it full of good times and interesting surprises.

One morning Mr. Marks said to him, "Day after tomorrow we'll be taking you home."

Home! Where had the time gone? But suddenly Segundo felt it would be very good to see his family again. He had so much to tell them!

HOME AGAIN 6

Segundo and Dean were helping to carry things to be loaded into the jeep. Everything must be ready for a very early start the next morning.

This time there would be five passengers. Two other students, Yolanda Cruz and Isabel Martinez, were going to help with the vacation school. Mr. Marks would take them all to the *barrio,* and the next day return to the mission.

Segundo carried out one last package and put it on the ground with the others. "Ai! Carlos," he said in alarm, "there will be no room for us with all this in the jeep."

Carlos laughed. "Have no fear, Segundo," he said. "I will show you how we make the jeep big enough for all."

Soon Carlos returned driving the jeep, and Segundo's eyes grew round with surprise.

Bouncing along behind it came a large box mounted on two wheels.

"How do you like our trailer?" asked Carlos. "We made it in the shop."

Segundo grinned. "Good!" he said. "Now I think we can go, too."

Mr. Marks and Carlos loaded the boxes and bags into the trailer. Then they spread a big piece of canvas over everything and fastened it with rope.

In the house Nancy and Mrs. Marks were busy.

"I wish I could send a present to Segundo's little sister Dona," said Nancy.

"A good idea," agreed her mother. "What do you think she might like?"

"I think she would like a doll," answered Nancy.

"Could you spare one of yours?" asked Mrs. Marks.

They went into Nancy's room to look at her family of four dolls. Nancy loved each one. She couldn't part with Rosalie, her newest doll, or Sue Ann, the most battered of all. That left Betsy, the doll that said "Ma-ma," and Baby Peggy.

70

"I think it had better be Peggy," said Nancy slowly.

"That's a good choice," said her mother. "Peggy is made of rubber and won't get broken on the journey. Let's make a package for Dona to open."

Next they thought it would be nice to have a gift for Maria as well. "Maria may be too big for dolls," said Mrs. Marks. "What would you think of a book?" So they found a book of Bible stories and pictures that seemed just right.

As they wrapped it, Mrs. Marks said, "Segundo has an older sister Angelina. Let me see what I can find for her."

She was soon back with a pretty scarf. So a third little package was made and added to Segundo's bundle.

The next morning everyone was up early. Soon after breakfast Carlos drove up with the jeep. The trailer no longer bounced as it had when empty, but rode smoothly at the rear. In the jeep sat Yolanda and Isabel.

"Time to go, everybody!" called Mr. Marks.

"Don't forget the presents," said Nancy.

"I won't," promised Segundo. He thanked Mrs. Marks. *"S-s-salamat,"* he said. "You have been very k-k-kind to me."

Mrs. Marks leaned over and gave Segundo a kiss. "It has been nice to have a second son for a while," she said.

It was hardest of all to say good-by to Dean.

"Good-by, Dean," said Segundo, and he climbed quickly into the jeep.

"So long, Segundo," said Dean. "Good-by, Daddy."

Suddenly Dean pulled his mother away to whisper a question in her ear.

"I think it's a very nice thought," she answered.

"Daddy!" cried Dean. "Wait just a second, please." He tore into the house. In a minute he was back, carrying a baseball and bat.

"Here, Segundo," he said, handing them to his friend. "I want you to take these."

"You m-m-mean to k-k-keep?" asked Segundo. He could hardly believe it.

"Sure," grinned Dean. "It's a present from me to you."

The jeep started moving. Segundo clutched his bat in one hand and his ball in the other. He was too surprised and excited to say thank you. But his shining eyes said it for him.

All morning they rode, with a brief stop for lunch. Later in the afternoon, when everyone was getting sleepy, Mr. Marks suggested that they play a game. That kept them interested for some time. It was fun, and everyone was in gay spirits. Suddenly Segundo noticed that they were driving into the market town.

"Look!" he exclaimed. "We are almost there!"

Now everything was familiar to Segundo—the narrow road, the winding river, the coconut grove. Then came the first houses of his own small *barrio*.

Mr. Marks stopped first at the home where Yolanda and Isabel were to stay. "We'll leave you to get acquainted," he said. "Carlos will pick you up later, so that you can help to get things ready for tomorrow."

Then they drove past the large house belonging to

Mr. Mansala, the landlord. They drove on past the path to the spring and Ramón's home, and then into the Garcia yard.

Mr. Marks honked the horn. At once there were shouts of welcome from the little *nipa* hut and Garcias seemed fairly to tumble from it. Maria first, then Dona, Angelina, Mother, Grandmother, and even Father, who had stopped work early so as to be there when the travelers arrived.

There were many cries of "Hello, hello," to everyone. Segundo greeted his mother and grandmother.

"You look well, Segundo," his mother said. "And your cheeks are rounder."

"I ate so much I got fat," laughed Segundo.

"How is your arm?" asked Grandmother.

"It was all well in a few days," replied Segundo. Then he remembered something and ran to the jeep. He got the baseball and bat. "Dean gave them to me," he said proudly.

Father took the bat in his hands and swung it up and down. "You'll have to teach me how to play," he said.

"Me, too!" said Maria, her black eyes dancing.

"Dean's little sister Nancy sent presents to you girls," said Segundo. He opened his bundle and found the three packages.

With wondering eyes the girls examined the pretty paper and ribbons.

"Open them," said Segundo. "The gifts are inside."

Maria got hers open first, and there were "Ohs" and "Ahs" from all as she turned the pages of the book.

"The stories I will read to all," she said. "Now show us your gift, Dona."

Dona slipped off the ribbon and opened her package.

"Oh, my!" she breathed softly. She looked at the little doll for a long moment and then held it to her cheek.

"My baby!" she said. "My beautiful baby!"

Now it was Angelina's turn. The scarf, too, was admired by all.

"I am sorry I could not bring presents for you,

Mother. And for Grandmother and for Father," said Segundo. "But I had no money."

His mother smiled. "You yourself are the best present you could bring us," she said. "We missed you, little son."

"How's Ongoy?" asked Segundo, remembering his pet.

"I think he is lonely," said Maria. "He seemed quiet while you were away. Come and see."

Segundo followed Maria to the mango tree. Ongoy sat under it, looking sad. Suddenly Segundo remembered what Carlos had said—"Poor little wild thing!"

"Come, Ongoy," he called. "Come and speak to me."

Ongoy ran to him, chattering a welcome, and jumped into his arms.

Next they had to call on Generál, and then Segundo must look under the house to make sure that the pigs and chickens were still there. Back in the house, they found that Mr. Marks and Carlos were to stay for the evening meal.

"We expected you," said Mother. "Everything is ready."

"It is a small thanks," said Father, "for all you have done for Segundo."

They did not linger over the meal. "We must hurry to the place of Mr. Mansala and make everything ready for tomorrow morning," said Mr. Marks.

"If I can help, I will gladly come along," said Father.

"Good!" said Mr. Marks.

"May I go too, please?" begged Segundo. "I can help, can't I, Carlos?"

"Sure," said Carlos. "If your mother says yes, there will be work for you, too."

When they reached the home of the landlord, Mr. Mansala came out and shook hands with Mr. Marks. Carlos went for Yolanda and Isabel. When all were there, Mr. Mansala led the way to the building he had offered for the vacation school. It was a long, low shed set in a grove of trees. The roof was of thatched *nipa,* the sides were open, and the floor was hard-packed earth.

Mr. Mansala smiled to himself as he opened the door.

Mr. Marks took one look. "Why," he exclaimed, "see what you have done for us! What a wonderful surprise!"

"I had it swept clean," said the landlord. "And my men made some tables and benches."

"We do not always meet such kindness," said Mr. Marks. "Why did you do it?"

"I do not follow your religion, Mr. Marks," said the landlord. "But when I lived in the city, my wife was taken to your hospital. The good doctor there saved her life. It will do no harm for the people here to learn what you have to teach."

Mr. Marks shook the landlord's hand. "Thank you, my friend," he said.

With so much done, it did not take long to get ready. Carlos and Mr. Garcia arranged the tables and benches. Mr. Marks found a large box to use for a table. Segundo carried things from the trailer, and the girls put them in place.

Yolanda found a beautiful picture of Jesus with

some children. She hung it above the box at the front. Isabel started to place an open Bible on the box.

"The box must have a cover," said Mr. Mansala. He hurried to the house and came back with a dark red cloth. It was spread over the box and the Bible was placed on top.

Everything was ready. They all stood back to admire their work.

"All it needs now is the children," said Mr. Marks.

Segundo could hardly wait for the next day to come.

The next morning Segundo, Maria, and Dona were among the first to arrive at the shed where the vacation school was to be held. Soon almost every child in the *barrio* who was old enough was there. Carlos and Yolanda and Isabel welcomed them all and spent a few minutes getting acquainted.

So began the first of many busy, happy mornings. Each day there were interesting things to hear, to see, and to do. The three teachers told many stories of Jesus, the Friend of all. Yolanda and Isabel taught new songs, while Carlos played the music on his guitar. The children learned Bible verses and drew pictures.

Together they made up a play about the Baby born in a stable and the shepherds who came to visit him. Josefina was Mary, Juan was Joseph, and Dona brought her baby doll to lay in the box that was the manger. Segundo and Ramón and Domingo were shepherds. Maria was the angel who came to tell them Jesus was born.

Maria made up her own speech. "Wake up, you sleepy shepherds!" she cried. "I have good news for you! The Little Lord Jesus is born in Bethlehem. Now hurry up and get there!"

No one laughed, and the shepherds hurried to the manger at the front of the shed. The play seemed real to everyone.

Each day there was a playtime, and Carlos taught many new games. It is no wonder that the children were all sorry when Friday came, for there would be no school on Saturday.

"Saturday will be a lonely day," said Segundo to Carlos.

"Perhaps the older boys would like to take a hike with me tomorrow," said Carlos.

"Am I an older boy?" asked Segundo quickly.

Carlos laughed. "You may come along," he said.

"Where are we going?" asked Segundo.

"Well," said Carlos, "Mr. Mansala told me about

a waterfall a few miles in the forest. I would like to see it."

"Do you think you can find it?" Segundo asked.

"Oh, yes," answered Carlos. "The landlord says there is a trail to a swinging bridge across the stream. He tells me it is used by the little forest people who have a village on the other side."

Segundo nodded. "The Negritos," he said. "They are little black people, and sometimes one of them comes to the store. But they won't talk to us, and they never stay long."

"They have their own language," said Carlos. "And they are very shy people."

That afternoon Carlos invited the older boys to go on the hike. "You must wear shoes for protection," he said. "And bring a lunch."

The next morning the boys began to gather before Carlos had finished breakfast. Segundo came first, then Manuel and Pablo, next Juan and Mario and Domingo, and last of all, Ramón, puffing because he was late. Each boy carried a lunch wrapped in a piece of banana leaf.

"O.K., fellows!" called Carlos. "We're off!"

Laughing and shouting, the boys followed him into the forest. The trail was clearly marked, but soon it became narrow. The trees closed in overhead, and vines seemed to try to trip them. But this only added to the fun.

They stopped to rest in a small open space. Segundo heard a slight movement in a tree above him. He looked up to see something small and dark swing quickly out of sight among the thick leaves. Could it have been a monkey? Segundo thought of Ongoy. Did Ongoy wish to be free like this?

In the meantime, Ramón had found a small lizard on a rock. He picked it up and, tiptoeing quietly behind Segundo, dropped it down the neck of his T shirt.

"Aow! Aow!" yelled Segundo, as he felt the tickling feet. He jumped so that he lost his balance and sat down.

Ramón doubled up laughing, but suddenly Segundo yelled louder than ever. "Ants!" he cried, as he danced around.

84

He had landed in an ant hill, and at once the big, angry ants swarmed out. Quickly Carlos and Mario brushed the ants off and shook out the lizard, but not before Segundo had received several bites.

"We'll fix you up, Segundo," said Carlos. He took a bottle of lotion from his first-aid kit and put some on each red spot. Soon the sting was gone.

"That Ramón!" muttered Segundo. "I'll get even yet!"

"Take it easy, little brother," said Carlos, giving him a wink that seemed to say, "Don't you remember we're partners in this getting even business?"

To the others Carlos said, "A joke isn't very funny when it makes someone uncomfortable. Come on, gang, I think we must be close to the waterfall by now."

Sure enough, soon they heard the sound of water tumbling over rocks. In a few minutes the trail led them to where a rushing mountain stream fell splashing and foaming over a rocky cliff into a deep ravine below. It was a beautiful sight, and for a moment the boys stood looking.

"Well," said Carlos, "this is worth a long hike!"

"May we cross the bridge, Carlos?" asked Domingo. Carlos examined the narrow swinging bridge over the ravine. It was cleverly made of bamboo pieces woven together with rope, and it had rope handrails. Carlos crossed over, testing the bridge as he went. He came back satisfied.

"It is safe," he said. "But remember, no funny business!"

As the boys walked slowly across, Segundo thought this the best part of the hike. Once over, they were all satisfied to return. To them the beautiful view was not as interesting as the fun of crossing the bridge.

"Look!" said Mario. "See that wide shelf down below us." Carlos and the boys looked and saw, about halfway down the side of the ravine, a broad shelf of rock.

"That's a nice place to eat our lunch," said Juan. "If we could only get there."

"Let's eat here in the clearing," laughed Carlos. "It's easier to reach."

The boys were hungry, and they gladly settled

down with their lunches. They had almost finished when Segundo cried, "Look, Carlos, quick! At the trail!"

They saw a small black man, not much taller than Segundo. He had kinky black hair, and he wore very little clothing. Over one shoulder he carried a coil of rope. He stood very still, gazing at the group of boys.

"Quiet, boys," said Carlos, getting slowly to his feet.

"Hello, Friend," he said, smiling.

But the stranger backed off. Quickly Carlos held out a banana. "Here," he said, walking forward. "We are friends."

The little man stood still until Carlos was within reach. Then he snatched the banana and ran for the bridge.

"He is shy!" said Carlos. "I suppose he has been to the *barrio* to buy that rope."

By this time the boys were on their feet, too—all but Ramón. As Pablo started to run forward for a better view of the stranger, Ramón stuck out a foot and tripped him. Pablo was up on his feet in a second, starting for Ramón. Ramón jumped up, too, and began to run, looking over his shoulder at Pablo.

Carlos turned at the commotion. "Watch it, Ramón!" he called sharply. "You are too close to the edge—"

But it was too late. The earth gave way under Ramón, and with a yell he disappeared over the edge of the ravine.

Carlos sprang for the bridge. "He's not killed, thank goodness!" For Ramón was still yelling loudly.

As Carlos and the boys looked down, they could see that Ramón had landed, head downward, on the ledge below them, with his feet up against the bank.

"Are you hurt, Boy?" called Carlos.

"Aow!" yelled Ramón, trying to wriggle free. "My foot is caught!"

Then they saw that somehow Ramón's foot was caught in a thick, twisting vine.

"Can't you pull your foot loose?" called Carlos.

"No! Get me out of here!" cried Ramón. But it

seemed as if all his squirming only tightened the vine around his ankle.

"Take it easy, Boy," said Carlos. "We'll get you out."

"Carlos," said Segundo, "here comes the little man."

They had forgotten the Negrito, who had been watching from the far end of the bridge. Now he came across to Carlos, holding out his coil of rope.

"*Salamat,* thank you," said Carlos, smiling at him as he took the rope. "This will help." The Negrito backed off to what he thought was a safe distance.

"Now if he could only get his foot free, we could pull him up," said Carlos.

"Get me out of here!" yelled Ramón.

"Carlos," said Segundo, "let me go down on the rope. I can cut the vines away from his foot, and you can pull us up one at a time."

Carlos looked at him. Segundo was the lightest one of the boys, and so would be the easiest to lower on the rope.

"You're not afraid, little brother?" he asked.

Segundo grinned. "You're going to hold the rope, aren't you?" he asked.

Now Carlos smiled. "It will be a swell way to get even," he said.

Carlos fastened his knife in Segundo's belt. Then he made a loop in one end of the rope. He showed Segundo how to sit in the loop and hold fast to the rope above.

"Here you go," he said, and with Mario and Juan helping, he lowered Segundo slowly to the ledge of rock. Segundo jumped from the rope and ran to Ramón. Taking the knife, he cut through the vine that held his foot.

With a grunt Ramón rolled free and sat up, leaning against the rock. "Aow!" he said. "I'm dizzy from being upside down."

Carlos decided it would be best to pull the boys up the slide where Ramón went down. He told them just how to fix the loop of the rope under Ramón's arms.

"You're going to walk up that slide while we pull," he said. "You'll be safe if you just hang onto the rope."

Carlos and the other boys left the bridge and went to the bank above Ramón.

"Ready, fellows, pull!" cried Carlos. "Start climbing, Ramón!"

Ramón's feet scrambled wildly as he made his way up the steep slope. In a minute he was over the top, scratched and dirty, but otherwise unhurt.

"Now you, Segundo," said Carlos, as he tossed the loop of rope down again. It was easy to pull Segundo up, for he seemed to weigh very little after Ramón.

Carlos looped the rope into a roll. The Negrito came to get it. Carlos handed him his knife, too, to show his thanks. The little man was delighted with the gift, and he smiled and nodded. Then he trotted across the bridge and disappeared.

Carlos patched up Ramón's scratches with his first-aid kit. Then he said, "That's about enough excitement for one day. Let's start home."

As the boys walked along the trail, Ramón dropped back beside Segundo. "Thanks for helping me," he said.

"That's O.K.," said Segundo.

But Ramón was not through. "I'm sorry about the lizard," he went on. He paused, and then began again. "And I didn't mean to let Ongoy get away that day."

"Forget it," said Segundo, with a grin.

Somehow Segundo had a very good feeling inside. Was this what Carlos meant about getting even? He glanced at Carlos, and once more the older boy winked at him. This time Segundo winked back.

8 CARLOS TELLS A STORY

The vacation school was almost at an end. The children had planned a closing program for the next meeting. Everyone was coming, for mothers and fathers and friends were curious to see what had kept their children so interested and happy. Mr. Marks and Mr. and Mrs. Mansala would be there. It would be an exciting time.

"We have a few minutes before we dismiss," Carlos was saying. "What would you like to do?"

"Tell us another story, please, Carlos," said Maria.

"Yes, tell us a story!" cried several others.

"Very well," said Carlos. He thought a moment. "I'll tell you the Bible story that I call my special story," he said. "When I finish, I'll tell you why."

The children settled back to listen.

"Long, long ago," began Carlos, "the people of Israel were having a bad time. They had been made slaves by the people of Egypt. The Egyptians were afraid their slaves might try to get free. So the king of Egypt decided that all the boy babies of the Israelites should be taken away from their families."

Carlos went on to tell how in one family a boy baby was born. His father, mother, big sister, and brother did their best to keep the baby a secret. Every time he cried or laughed, someone ran to quiet him.

But the baby soon grew bigger, and they could hide him no longer.

Carlos told how the mother then made a little basket boat. She put the baby in it. She took it to the river's edge and hid it among the tall reeds there.

"You see," Carlos said, "the king's daughter came each day to bathe at this spot. The mother felt that if the princess could only see her baby, she would want him. The mother told Sister Miriam to hide nearby and watch what happened."

"What did happen?" asked Maria.

Carlos smiled. "The princess came," he said. "She found the basket boat floating in the water. When she saw the baby, she fell in love with him, just as the mother had hoped.

" 'A beautiful baby!' she said. 'I shall keep him. I'll call him Moses.'

"Then Miriam ran to her. 'Shall I find a nurse for your baby?' she asked.

" 'Yes,' said the princess, and Miriam ran to bring her own mother.

" 'Keep this baby and nurse him for me,' said the princess. 'When he is old enough, I shall take him to the palace.'

"And that," ended Carlos, "is what happened. Moses was allowed to stay with his own family while he was little. When he was older, the princess took him to the palace and educated him. But Moses never forgot his own people. When he was a man, God chose him to lead his people to another country where they could be free."

The children sat back satisfied.

Then Segundo remembered something. "You said

you would tell us why this is your special story," he reminded Carlos.

"Oh, yes," said Carlos. "Well, this is quite a long story. When I was a very little boy," he went on, "I was found in a boat in the river, too, like Moses. No one knew how I got there, but it was after a bad storm—a typhoon. Some men coming down the river in another boat found me."

"Couldn't you tell them who you were?" asked Maria.

"I was only about three years old," said Carlos. "I didn't know where I lived. I could only say my name was Carlos. One of the men, whose name was Cruz, took me home as his son."

"Then what happened?" asked Maria. No child wanted to go home now. This was as exciting as any story they had ever heard, and it had happened to someone they knew.

"Oh," laughed Carlos, "I told you it was a long story. Father and Mother Cruz were very good to me, but a year or so after I went to live with them, the war came. Then as you know, all our people had a very hard time. Father Cruz went to war and never came back. When the war ended, I was about as big as Segundo here. But I was sick. Mother Cruz heard that the mission hospital on this island had opened again, so she took me there. Soon afterwards she died. When I got better, Dr. and Mrs. Brown kept me with them until I was old enough to live with the boys in the mission school.

"I tell you this," said Carlos, "to show you that God has wonderful ways of caring for us. I think God saved Moses so he could help his people. I hope," he ended with a smile, "that God will show me a way to help my people, too."

"I think you are helping right now," said Maria.

"That is enough about me," said Carlos. "What shall we sing?"

Segundo did not open his mouth to sing. He did not hear a word of the song. A wonderful thought had come to him, and he kept turning it over in his mind. As soon as the children were dismissed, he hurried to Carlos.

"C-C-Carlos, I have to t-t-talk to you," he said.

Carlos looked at Segundo and saw that he was excited.

"Wait a few minutes while I help put things away," he said. "Then we'll talk."

Segundo stood waiting and thinking. His mind was full of just one idea.

Soon Carlos was ready. He led Segundo to a quiet place behind his tent. "Now, let's have it, little brother," he said. "Is something worrying you?"

"Y-y-yes. N-no. I d-d-don't know," stammered Segundo. Then it came out. "Carlos, c-c-could you be my brother?"

Carlos smiled. "I thought we adopted each other some time ago," he said.

But Segundo shook his head. "I d-don't mean that," he said. "I mean my real brother Carlos who was lost."

Surprise spread over Carlos' face. "Why, that couldn't be possible!" he said. "I thought your brother was drowned."

"No one knows for sure," said Segundo. "There was a bad typhoon, just as you said. Mother and

Father were away. They had Angelina with them. Carlos stayed home with Grandmother. Our house blew down. Lots of houses and trees blew down. Grandmother was hurt, and Carlos disappeared. Everyone thought he was blown into the river."

Carlos put his arm around Segundo's shoulder. "I never heard that story," he said. "What a sad time for your family! But Segundo, I don't think I could have been that little boy. There have been lots of typhoons, you know. And Father Cruz lived on another island." Then Carlos paused. "It is true," he added slowly, "that Father Cruz sometimes came to this island to work. He was a guide for Americans and others who wanted to fish or explore."

"He might have been on our river," said Segundo.

"I don't know the name of the river where I was found," said Carlos.

"Do you remember how you took the right path to the spring?" Segundo asked.

"Oh, that could happen by accident," said Carlos.

"But why did you call our carabao Capitán?" persisted Segundo. " We used to have one by that name."

"Yes," said Carlos thoughtfully. "It is strange how that name came to me. And it is strange how I always feel so much at home with your family."

"C-C-Carlos," Segundo said, "everyone says I look just like you."

Carlos sat looking at Segundo, who might indeed have been a younger and smaller copy of himself. "I just can't believe it," he said. "But I'm going to find out. First I must talk to your grandmother. Then I must go to the island where Father Cruz lived. There was another man with him when I was found."

"Please be my real brother, Carlos," begged Segundo.

Carlos put his hands on the smaller boy's shoulders. "I hope it will work out that way," he said. "But you mustn't count on it. Until we can be sure, let's keep this to ourselves. We wouldn't want to get everyone stirred up and then disappoint them. Will you keep it as our secret?"

Segundo nodded. "I won't tell anyone," he said.

"Good boy," smiled Carlos. "Now let's go find your grandmother."

Grandmother was alone in the little house. She smiled as the two came in, for Carlos was a favorite with her.

"Ah!" she said. "To think our little Carlos might have been a fine young man like you if he had lived!"

"Tell me about your Carlos," said Carlos gently. "Tell me how you lost him."

"It was a very bad time," said Grandmother. "Segundo's mother had gone to her own *barrio* to care for her mother, who was sick. Baby Angelina she took with her. When the mother was better, my son went to get his wife. Carlos stayed here with me."

"How old was the little boy?" asked Carlos.

"A little over three," said Grandmother. "A fine, strong one, Carlos was. He loved to play in the water, and he climbed in and out of our boat without fear.

"The day after my son left, the typhoon came. It was a very bad one, and for three days it stormed. We could hear the crashing of the trees as they were blown down.

"I was afraid our little house would go," said

Grandmother, "and most of the time Carlos and I stayed under it, with the pigs and chickens. The third night we were tired and wet, and I thought the storm was ending. So we climbed the ladder into the house and fell asleep." Grandmother wiped her eyes.

"Then what happened?" urged Carlos.

"The storm grew worse while we were asleep," said Grandmother. "There was a great crash, and then I knew nothing for a long time. When I came to, I was lying by the river's edge. Our house was gone, and I could not see Carlos anywhere. I hunted and called, but I could not find him."

"Was the typhoon over?" asked Carlos.

"Yes," said Grandmother. "Everything was quiet. But everywhere trees were down, and houses were destroyed. Everyone was in trouble, but some of the neighbors came to help hunt for Carlos. Later that day my son came home. For several days he searched. Our boat was gone, and we thought that if Carlos had been blown toward the boat, he might have climbed in, as he did at play. My son searched far down the river. At last he found the boat, caught in some branches, but it was empty. That was our last hope."

"Do you remember when this happened?" asked Carlos.

"I can never forget," said Grandmother, and she told him the date.

"And now," she said, "that is enough of this sad story. You can imagine how happy we were, some years later, when another baby boy who looked like Carlos came to us. His father named him Pedro, but we were so pleased to have a second son that we have always called him Segundo." She smiled at Segundo.

"Thank you for telling me all this," said Carlos, as he rose to go.

Segundo followed him to the bamboo fence.

"What do you think about it, Carlos?" he asked.

"I don't know what to think," said Carlos slowly. "But I'm going to find out all that I can about myself." He smiled at Segundo's anxious face.

"Let's forget it now until our program is over," he said. "It's our secret and we'll just have to wait."

Segundo nodded. But it would not be easy to wait.

9 SO LONG TO WAIT

The next day was a busy one for the children and their teachers. Everything must be made ready for the evening program. The boys and girls arranged a display of things they had made. They went over the songs and Bible stories and verses they would share. Mario practiced his speech of welcome.

Finally it was time for the closing worship. Yolanda told them one last story about how Jesus asked his friends to go on with his work. Carlos talked to them about how they could be friends of Jesus today.

Ever since he had visited the mission, Segundo had known what he wanted to do when he grew up. He wanted to be a doctor, to help those who were sick. It was a new idea—that he could begin now to help others and be a friend of Jesus.

No one took a long *siesta* that day. The children began to gather again long before time for the program. Segundo and Maria and Dona were among the first to come. Segundo wore a fresh white T shirt and his best shorts. The girls wore their red flowered dresses.

Because so many were early, Mr. Marks found a crowd ready to welcome him when he drove in. From the moment he arrived, he was busy. First, the boys and girls showed him their work. Then Carlos took him over behind his tent for a talk. When they came back, a committee of three men, Segundo's father and two others, were waiting to talk with him also.

As the men talked, the guests began to arrive. The boys and girls led their admiring friends from table to table as they showed their work.

At last everyone was seated. The program began. They sang a hymn, and Mario gave his speech of welcome. Carlos explained that during their two weeks together they had been learning of Jesus and the things he taught.

The children gave their first play, about the Baby Jesus and the shepherds. It seemed very real and beautiful.

After the play several boys and girls told stories of Jesus. There were more songs and Bible verses that had been learned. It was dark by the time they were ready for their second play, which was called "The Good Neighbor." Mr. Marks quietly moved the jeep and turned on the lights to make a path of light across the front of the shed. At last the program came to an end.

"Hasn't it been wonderful?" Mrs. Garcia whispered to Mrs. Santos. Mrs. Santos nodded as she whispered back, "All that our children have learned has been good. I am glad now that I allowed mine to come."

Mr. Marks told the boys and girls that they had done well, and he hoped they would keep on trying to be friends of Jesus every day. Then he spoke to the older people.

"Some of you," he said, "have asked if we could start a church in this village so that you will have a place to worship God and to learn more about Jesus. That is a very good wish. All of us at the mission want to help you. But," he went on, "it must be your church. You will have to find the land and build it. You will have to give part of your rice and coconuts to support it. You must think and talk and pray about it. When you are ready, we will find a pastor for you."

At that moment Mr. Mansala stood up in the back of the shed.

"Mr. Marks," he said, "as you know, I feel very friendly to your work. I have listened to our children tonight, and I am pleased with what they have learned. If the people of this *barrio* wish to start a church, I will give for that purpose the land on which this shed stands and the shed itself."

Everyone clapped and cheered as Mr. Mansala sat down.

"We are fortunate to have such a friend," said Mr. Marks. "You men can easily turn this shed into a church by building sides and putting in doors and windows.

"And now," he went on, "I have more news. As you know, our three young teachers return tomorrow to the mission. But Carlos tells me he would like to come back in a week or so and spend the rest of his vacation in your *barrio*. Our friend, Mr. Mansala, has offered him work through the week.

"Each Sunday Carlos will hold Sunday school here, to which all are invited. Carlos is not a pastor," smiled Mr. Marks, "but he has had long Christian training in the mission. At the end of his vacation, we will come again. If you are sure then that you want a church, we will help you."

Segundo clapped and cheered more loudly than anyone. Of course, it would be wonderful to have a church, but he was cheering most of all because Carlos would return. Even if Carlos did not find out he was Segundo's brother, Segundo would be happy to have him back.

The morning after the program, Segundo slipped out of the house very early to see his friends off.

"Good-by, Carlos," he called, as the jeep started. "I'm g-glad you're coming back."

"So am I," Carlos smiled. "Good-by, Segundo. I'll be back as soon as I find out—all there is to find out."

Segundo knew Carlos was talking about their secret.

It was hard to keep such an important thing to himself, when he thought about it so much, but Segundo did it. He found it was easier for him when he kept busy.

He went with his father to work in the coconut grove of Mr. Mansala. He liked to help with the coconut harvest.

When the trees were not too high, a man with a knife fastened to the end of a long bamboo pole reached up and cut the nuts loose. The tallest trees had to be climbed. Some of the men were very clever about going up them. Segundo was a good climber, too, but his father would not allow him to climb the highest ones.

There was other work he could do. As the coconuts fell, they were loaded into the cart. When the cart was full, it was driven to the river's edge. There

the coconuts were piled on a flatboat to be taken away and sold.

Segundo had more time for Ongoy, too. He worried about the little monkey, who sat hunched up by the tree. But when Segundo arrived, Ongoy came to life and dashed to his side.

Segundo played with him every day. Often he tied Ongoy's rope around his own waist, and then the monkey would run along beside him or ride happily on his shoulder. Always he scolded when he had to be tied to his tree. One afternoon Ongoy fastened his skinny little arms around Segundo's neck and clung tightly, whimpering like an unhappy child.

"Poor little fellow!" said Segundo. "You don't like to be tied up, do you?"

Segundo thought of the monkeys he had seen in the forest. He remembered what Carlos had said when he first saw Ongoy—"Poor little wild thing!"

"Do you want so much to be free?" asked Segundo. Ongoy's small wrinkled face looked up at him sadly.

Slowly Segundo unfastened the leather strap

around Ongoy's body. The strap, with the rope attached, dropped to the ground. Segundo loosened Ongoy's paws, like little hands in black kid gloves, from around his neck. He placed Ongoy on the ground. Then he stepped back so that Ongoy could see that he was free.

For a moment Ongoy sat and stared at Segundo in surprise. Then with an excited little squeal, he scrambled up the trunk of a big tree nearby. He paused on the lowest branch and looked down at Segundo, chattering all the while.

"Good-by, Ongoy," called Segundo.

He told no one what he had done. It was almost dark when Dona came racing into the house.

"Segundo!" she shouted. "Ongoy is gone again!"

"I know," said Segundo. "I let him go."

"You did!" exclaimed Maria. "I thought you liked Ongoy so much!"

"I d-did. I do," said Segundo. "That's why I did it. He wanted to be free."

A DREAM COME TRUE 10

Segundo missed Ongoy more than he would say. One afternoon he lay on the ground beside the mango tree, waiting for the evening meal. Where was Ongoy now, he wondered.

Then his thoughts turned to Carlos. Carlos had been gone less than two weeks, but to Segundo it seemed forever. When would he come back? Would he find out that he was really Carlos Garcia? If not, how could Segundo bear it?

Segundo sat up to see what was coming down the road. It was Ramón's father in his carabao cart, returning from the town. Someone sat beside him. It was not Ramón.

Could it be— Segundo raced for the opening in the bamboo fence. Yes, it was Carlos!

"Hi, Carlos!" he cried.

"Stop, Nuang!" called Ramón's father.

Carlos jumped to the ground. "Thank you for the lift, my friend," he smiled at Ramón's father.

"Glad to do it," answered Ramón's father, smiling. "Hungh, Nuang! Get on home!"

Segundo was tugging at Carlos' bag. He was almost afraid to ask the important question, but he had to know.

"C-C-Carlos," he said, "wh-what did you find out?"

"Good news, little brother," smiled Carlos. "I found what I wanted to know."

Segundo was so happy he couldn't talk. He wanted to laugh and shout, yet for some reason he wanted to cry, too. He dropped the bag and turned two somersaults.

Carlos laughed. "I feel something like that myself," he said. "Let us break it gently to the family. I do hope they believe it."

"They'll believe it all right," said Segundo.

Angelina came to the door. "Come, Segundo," she called. "It's time to eat." Then she saw Carlos and called in welcome, "It is good to see you, Carlos!"

The others were now crowding to the door, smiling.

"Come in," said Mother, and Father shook his hand.

"Get a plate for Carlos, Maria," said Grandmother.

"I'm always here when it is time to eat," said Carlos.

"No one is more welcome," smiled Mother. "It seems as if you are one of us."

Carlos and Segundo looked at each other and smiled.

Soon everyone was eating, the older ones at the low table and the children seated on the floor. No one cared to go outside this time.

"So you have been away on a trip?" Father asked.

"Yes," answered Carlos. "I went back to the place where I lived before coming to the mission. I wanted to see if I could learn something of my real family."

"Maria told us how you were found when you were a small boy," said Mother. "I hope you found out what you wanted to know."

"I think so," said Carlos. "I will tell you my story."

"Now it's coming," thought Segundo.

"Perhaps Maria told you," began Carlos, "that my foster father, Pablo Cruz, was lost in the war. Mother Cruz died soon after she placed me in the mission. So I could not talk to them. But there was another man named José, who was with Pablo the day I was found. He was the one I hoped to see."

"Did you find him?" asked Angelina.

"Yes," said Carlos. "I had a long talk with him. He told how he and Pablo often worked as guides for men who wanted to travel up our rivers.

"This day," went on Carlos, "they were bringing an American downriver. They had been delayed by the typhoon. The river was high, and many things were floating by in the water. They came to a small boat caught in a tree in the river. José said they caught sight of a child lying in the bottom of the boat. As they came close, their boat bumped into the one that was caught, and the little boy woke up. That is how they found me."

"But couldn't they find out where you lived?"

asked Mother. "Couldn't they find your home? Think how your mother must have felt—if she was alive."

"That is the strange part of the story," said Carlos. "José said that for miles back they had passed no *barrio*. The American was in a great hurry to catch a plane to the States. He decided they must go on to the airport. When he left, he gave Pablo and José some money to use in trying to find my family."

"And they never did?" asked Angelina.

"I am not sure how hard they tried," answered Carlos, "but José said they went back up the river for quite a distance. They asked everyone they saw if they had heard of a little boy being lost, but no one had. Then they decided that my parents must have been lost in the typhoon. Pablo Cruz, who had always wanted a son, took me home. Before long, I forgot I was not Carlos Cruz.

"I might never have come back to this island," went on Carlos, "if the war had not come and changed things for the Cruz family."

Suddenly Father leaned forward. "Why do you

say 'back to this island'?" he demanded. "Where was this river?"

"I was found on the river that goes past this village," said Carlos, "but far downstream."

Everyone was staring at Carlos now. Everyone seemed afraid to ask another question.

Segundo could stand it no longer. "It's true! It's true!" he cried. "This is our own Carlos!" He jumped up and stood behind Carlos with his arms around the older boy's shoulders.

Father asked quickly, "Did this José tell you the date when you were found?"

Carlos smiled. "It was July 14, 1940," he said.

Mother and Grandmother were crying.

"That is the day our Carlos was lost," Grandmother said.

Father seized Carlos by the hand. "Carlos," he said, "you are my son!"

Everyone was smiling now. "If you're not sure—" Carlos began.

"Sure?" exclaimed Grandmother. "Have we not always felt it in our hearts?"

"I know a test," smiled Mother, "though we do not need it. My little Carlos had a small brown mark, shaped like a heart, on his left shoulder. I think he would always have it."

Still smiling, Carlos slipped his shirt down over one shoulder. Segundo did not want to look. Suppose there was no mark there!

"See!" shouted Maria. "There is the little brown heart!"

Carlos kissed his mother's hand and then his grandmother's. He turned to the girls and said, "Imagine getting three sisters, all at once!"

"And a brother!" cried Segundo. "A brother, too!"

"You bet, a brother!" said Carlos, giving him a friendly poke. "If it hadn't been for your second son here, your first son might never have found his way home."

So then it had to be told—how Segundo got the idea from Carlos' story, and how he made Carlos believe it might be true.

"The most important thing to me," said Carlos, "was that so many people said Segundo and I looked just alike. And I believe we both resemble you, Father."

Father sat up proudly. "A man is fortunate to have two such sons," he said.

"To say nothing of three beautiful daughters!" laughed Carlos, swinging Dona up in his arms.

"We must invite our neighbors to a feast, a *lecho-nada*," said Father, "and tell them our good news."

"Yes, we will roast a pig," said Mother.

"And cook some chicken and rice," said Grand-mother.

"And bake some sweet potatoes and pick mangoes and bananas," added Angelina.

They talked a long time, as if they wanted to make up in this one evening for all the years they did not have Carlos. Carlos told how he planned to help farmers to raise better crops when he finished study-ing with Mr. Marks.

"Perhaps we could work together, Father," he said. "We could make this *barrio* a center for good farming and Christian teaching. We would do much to make life better and easier for our people."

"You must begin to teach me the things you learn at the mission," said Father, "so that I will be ready."

"Some day," said Segundo, "I want to go to the mission school, too. I want to learn to be a d-d-doctor. C-can I do that, Carlos?"

Carlos looked at the smaller boy. "Of course you can," he said. "It takes years of study and lots of hard work to learn to be a doctor, but you can do it. I'll help you all I can, little brother. And the mission will help you, too."

At last Mother said, "These children must get to bed. Carlos, we can only give you a *banig* on the floor."

"Fine," said Carlos. "I'll go outside till the children are asleep."

"I'll go with you," said Father.

Segundo would like to have gone, too, but Mother shook her head. Besides, he was very sleepy. He spread his *banig* on the floor.

"Good night, Segundo," said Mother. "You have helped to bring us great happiness this day."

"Good night," said Segundo. He did not want this

wonderful day to end. But there would be tomorrow.
Every day would be wonderful with Carlos home.

From outside came the sound of Father's guitar.
Segundo heard his father's and Carlos' voices as they
sang:

> My *nipa* hut is very small,
> But the foods that I grow—
>   see it houses them all!

TO HELP YOU UNDERSTAND THE STORY

SOME WORDS YOU WILL FIND

bamboo (bam-BOO), a tall, treelike grass with hollow woody stem

banig (bah-NIG), a sleeping mat of woven palm leaves or straw

barrio (BAH-ree-oh), a village

bolo (BOH-loh), a large knife with a handle of wood or horn

carabao (kah-rah-BAH-oh), a water buffalo

lechonada (leh-choh-NAH-dah), a feast at which roast pig is served

mango (MANG-goh), a fruit

nipa (NEE-pah), a palm used for thatching houses

paro (PAH-roh), a parrot

rice paddy, a rice field

salamat (sah-LAH-maht), thank you

siesta (see-EHS-tah), a midday rest or nap

sinco (SING-koh), a nickel

NAMES

Angelina	ahn-heh-LEE-nah
Capitán	kah-pee-TAHN
Carlos	KAHR-lohs
Cruz	krooz
Domingo	doh-MEEN-goh
Dona	DOH-nah
Filberto	feel-BEHR-toh
Garcia	gahr-SEE-ah

Generál	heh-neh-RAHL
Isabel	EEZ-ah-bell
José	hoh-SEH
Josefina	hoh-seh-FEE-nah
Juan	hwahn
Mansala	mahn-SAH-lah
Manuel	muh-noo-ELL
Maria	mahr-yah
Mario	mahr-yoh
Martinez	mahr-TEE-nehs
Negrito	neh-GREE-toh (a Negro dwarf of a forest tribe)
Nuang	noo-AHNG (a word for carabao)
Ongoy	ong-GOY
Pablo	PAH-bloh
Pacito	pah-SEE-toh
Panay	pah-NIGH
Pedro	PAY-droh
Ramón	rah-MOAN
Reyes	RAY-yes
Rivera	ree-VEH-rah
Santos	SAHN-tohs
Segundo	seh-GUHN-doh (the second one)
Yolanda	yoh-LAHN-dah

TYPE: FOURTEEN POINT CASLON, LEADED SIX POINTS · COM-
POSITION, PRINTING, AND BINDING: QUINN & BODEN COM-
PANY, INC., RAHWAY, NEW JERSEY · JACKETS AND PAPER
COVERS: AFFILIATED LITHOGRAPHERS, INC., NEW YORK

Format by Dorothy Papy
Binding by Louise E. Jefferson